a prairie boy's winter and summer

paintings and story by William Kurelek

Tundra Books, Montreal

a prairie boy's winter © William Kurelek, 1973

Printing history

1973 First printing, Tundra Montreal
First US printing, Houghton-Mifflin
A *New York Times* Best Illustrated Book
A *New York Times* Outstanding Book of the Year
Second Canadian printing
Second US printing

1974 Canadian Association of Children's Librarians' Best Illustrated Book of the Year
Children's Book Council Showcase Book Award, New York
Boston Globe/Horn Book Honor Book

1973-4 One of only 4 books, out of 2000, chosen by 3 independent juries (retailers, designers and children) of the
American Institute of Graphic Arts as best children's books published in US and Canada

1975 Third Canadian printing
UK edition, William Collins Sons
Featured in Third International Survey of Children's Book Illustration, *Graphis*, The Graphis Press, Zurich, Switzerland

1977 Third US printing

1978 First Canadian paperback edition
Norwegian edition, Den norske Bokklubben
Swedish edition, Carlsen
Featured in Special Exhibition, Canada House, London, England

a prairie boy's summer © William Kurelek, 1975

Printing history

1975 First printing, Tundra Montreal
First US printing, Houghton-Mifflin
A *New York Times* Outstanding Book of the Year

1976 Children's Book Council Showcase Book Award, New York
Canadian Association of Children's Librarians' Best Illustrated Book of the year
IODE Book of the Year
UK edition, William Collins Sons

1978 Norwegian edition, Den norske Bokklubben

ISBN 0-88776-106-2

Published in Canada by Tundra Books of Montreal, Montreal, Quebec H3G 1J6
Printed in Belgium in association with the Norwegian Book Club

a prairie boy's winter

paintings and story by William Kurelek

For everyone who ever spent a winter on the prairies
— and for all the others who wonder what it was like

a prairie boy's winter

1. Crows Leaving Before Winter

It was chilly. The skies hung heavy and gray as William, his brother,
John, and his sister, Winnie, joined other children on the highway, schoolbound.

The crows had been loitering around in great flocks, quarreling, cawing,
and raiding farmers' cornfields. Now they were finally leaving. They flew south
every fall about this time to escape the harsh prairie winter. In the cow
pasture the leaves had fallen from the white poplars and the oaks, leaving the
crows' nests bare in the high branches.

It would be five months before one of those noisy black birds came flapping
back over the pasture bush to announce the end of winter.

2. The First Snowfall

William behaved like children all over the world at the first snowfall.
He became giddy with excitement and held his mouth open to
catch the first big juicy flakes spiraling slowly downward.

Immediately after school, William and Winnie were sent by their mother to
fetch the cows. For the past few days the animals had been huddling
under the straw pile to keep warm. From now until spring they would
remain in the barn, apart from a brief daily visit to the water trough.

This year William's father had managed to lay up plenty of cattle feed for the
winter. Two large clover stacks had been built beside the warmer south
side of the barn, and a silo hole had been filled with ensilage and
covered over. Ensilage is finely chopped green corn that has partly fermented
under its own weight. Cows go crazy over their daily ration of it —
one forkful per cow — just as cats do over catnip. But their main dinner
was hay, and some of that was already in the hayloft.

3. Calling Pigs to Feed

The first snowfall was heavy and the next day the sun shone on a dazzling white, cold landscape.

William helped his mother carry feed to the pigpen. While she poured it into the trough, he counted the pigs as they came out of the straw. His mother called, "Tsyok, tsyok, tsyok, tsyow," which the pigs understood as, "Food's on!" The pail had to be empty before the first pig reached the trough, because pigs are so greedy and bad-mannered they climb into the trough with all four feet. Then you couldn't put any more feed in unless you poured it over their heads.

Bad as their table manners are, pigs do keep their living quarters clean, contrary to what most people believe. William, John, and Winnie saw this for themselves later when the pigs had been hauled away to market. The cave in the middle of the straw stack that they reached by a tunnel, was cozy and perfectly clean. In summer, the pigpen was overgrown with weeds so tall the children couldn't even see each other over the tops. But in winter, the dried-up stalks of the weeds could be broken off and used as spears in tribal warfare.

4. Fox and Geese

The games of farm children were handed down from generation to generation. One of them was always played at school after the first snowfall. By shuffling their feet, the children traced a large pie-shaped design in the snow, clear down to the dried-up brown grass. William and his friends called an eight-piece pie Fox and Geese, and a four-piece pie Cat and Mice. Usually these pies, or wheels with spokes, were tramped out in a clear unspoiled stretch of snow just outside the schoolyard which the children had to crawl through the school fence to reach.

The game was already in full swing. William snagged his jacket on the barbed wire in his rush to join. A fox had been chosen — or had volunteered — and he chased anyone he thought he could tag. The tagged one would then become the fox.

It was no fun being a fox if you were slow, because you got teased a lot. "Nyah! Nyah! Can't catch me!" Of course, everyone, fox and goose, had to stay on the lines of the wheel or pie, and it was hard to pass anyone without falling into the snow and being disqualified. Some tried to sneak up as close as possible to the fox and then escape him narrowly. Others made faces at him from the safety of home. Home was the hub of the wheel, and there the geese were safe.

5. Rink Making

William didn't really like hockey or any other rough sport because he wasn't strong, athletic, or quick. But when the time came to make a hockey rink, the hockey lovers persuaded everyone to pitch in and help.

The work could not begin until the ground was frozen hard under the snow. Then an area was marked out between the school barn and the pump, and the snow was cleared right down to the grass. It was pushed or shoveled to the sides to make a shallow bank around the rink. Then, using all the pails that could be gathered together and the old copper boiler off the school stove, the children flooded the rink with water beginning at the corner farthest from the pump. The water steamed up for only a few minutes before the cold of the ground and the air gripped it solid.

By using both recesses and the noon hour, they could get the first shell of ice laid in one day but it would be very bumpy. The rink had to be reflooded at least once a week to keep the bumps covered, and, of course, it had to be cleared after every snowfall.

6. Hockey Hassles

William dreaded arguments, and there always seemed to be arguments in hockey games. A common cause was the lack of a net. For goal posts, two oak poles had been driven into the ground before flooding, but without a net it was often difficult to tell which side of the post the puck had gone. William was a poor skater and preferred not to play on skates, so he was made goalie. This put him right in the center of the arguments. All the boys joined in. Sometimes, one side pretended to be generous and give in on a goal. But usually the side that shouted the loudest and longest won the point.

William made his own shin pads by cutting off old trouser legs and sewing them up and down at regular, spaced intervals. Into these narrow pockets he slipped thin slats from apple boxes and then attached the pads to his legs with rubber sealing rings from his mother's preserve jars.

The goalie's stick was easier to make than those of the offensive players. William had only to nail two layers of support slats on the side of a board. But other boys spent days examining branches and small trees on their way home from school in the hope of finding one suitable for a hockey stick. Some simply nailed two thin boards together neatly at the right angle, and hoped they would not come apart at a crucial moment during the game. A lucky few got real hockey sticks for Christmas. Jesse, the star player, was among the lucky and it was often he who argued with William over which side of the post the puck went.

7. Will He or Won't He?

On the frozen sea of snow that stretched across farmlands broken only by barbed-wire fences, prairie boys would find jack-rabbit trails. And their eyes lit up: "Game!"

William and John could not afford bullets for their father's .22 rifle. Even if they could have, the walk knee-deep in bush snow and the long, cold lying-in-wait were very difficult. Nor was it easy to spot a rabbit in the first place because of his white winter coat. So what was simpler than to set a snare?

On nights when the traps were out, William would lie awake in bed imagining the next unsuspecting rabbit loping down the trail in the lonely winter stillness under the Northern Lights. "Will he or won't he get caught?" he wondered. What a thrill it was for him and John in the morning as they inspected their little "trap line" to find a frozen rabbit here, another there. Frozen, unskinned rabbits sold for twenty-five cents; four rabbits fetched a dollar, a fantastic sum for an eleven- or twelve-year-old boy in those hard years.

8. Hauling Hay

No matter how much hay was laid up in the barn, there was never enough to last the winter.

William liked the drive across the frozen fields to the hay stacks, but not the work after he arrived there. The stack usually had a cap of snow packed into it by the wind and glazed hard by the sun of warmer winter days. The cap had to be broken with fork or shovel and stripped off; otherwise one would be forever tugging at strands of hay rooted deep in the snow and ice.

William had built many of the stacks himself in the summer, and he had learned that it didn't pay to do the work carelessly. If the stacks were not made properly, rain would seep in and cause moldy patches — and bring a scolding from his father.

The horses cooled off during the loading. Icicles were hanging from their nostrils by the time the last pitchfork was stuck into the crown of the load and William's father took the reins and called out, "Giddap!" He and William turned their collars up and wrapped the horse blanket around themselves, for the heat and sweat worked up during the loading could bring on a chill if they were not well covered. Hoarfrost coated their eyebrows as they set out on the slow wobbly ride homeward.

9. Skiing Behind the Hayrack

Sometimes the children turned the job of hauling hay into a sport. Where William first got the idea of several people skiing side by side behind the hay wagon he could not tell you. There were no lakes near their prairie farm and he had never seen water-skiers. But one day he attached a long piece of hay wire to the back of his father's rack with a stick at the other end to hold on to. As the rack headed down the road, going at a trot pace because it was still empty, it pulled him along too, at wire's length. Winnie and John then joined in with their tow wires. Sliding behind the hayrack, the skiers discovered that their speed increased simply by pointing their skis off to the side of the road. Extra danger and thrills could be got by actually skiing right onto the roadside fields. They crossed the barbed-wire fence on the back of a high snowdrift, and hoped that another big drift farther along would allow them a chance to get back onto the road.

William tried carving his first skis out of boards, but he could never get enough curl-up at the front and they caused tumbles at the slightest snag. Finally, the three children persuaded their parents to buy them the cheap willow skis they had seen advertised in the mail-order catalogue. The binding was the simplest kind: a single strap passing through a flat hole in the middle of the ski. It was usually at the hole that the skis finally broke, but not before they had given a lot of pleasure.

10. Watering Cows in Winter

Before William's father made a pipeline from the pump house to the barn and installed water troughs in the mangers, the dairy herd had to be watered at an outside trough. Even when it was snowing and blowing, the cows had to go out, for eating dry hay and chop for twenty-four hours made them very thirsty. Because it was such an ordeal for both man and beast, the chore was limited to once a day, and the children had to help.

John would undo the stanchions in late afternoon and chase the whole herd into the bitter cold outside. The cows would hunch up their backs and charge toward the water trough to get the whole experience over with as quickly as possible. William, dressed in his warmest red mackinaw, worked the trough, hacking away at the crust of ice formed the day before. Meanwhile, his mother thawed out the pump with a kettle of hot water so that fresh water could be pumped in. She tried not to pump more water than the cows would drink, for any that was left would freeze solid and only have to be chopped out the next day. The water was so cold that now and then as the cows drank they had to lift their teeth out of it when the chill became too painful.

11. Chasing a Chicken in the Snow

Another chore that the children helped with was cleaning chicken manure out of the coop. This was easy work compared to barn cleaning, for chicken droppings were light and much mixed with straw. Usually a fresh sunny day was chosen for the job.

Chickens are jumpy. If anyone cleaning under them makes an unexpected move, the whole flock will fly into the air. One chicken might even fly out the door to the glistening snow. Then, William's mother would yell, "William! Winnie! Come here, catch the one that got away!" Now, there is nothing so stupid as a chicken. You can't drive it, for it does not follow a straight course away from humans, as cows or horses or geese do. Nor will it let itself be caught. The best you can do, as William found out from experience, is to keep the chicken moving until it is worn out. Then you hedge in, and pounce! If you're lucky, you can grab it by the leg and carry it squawking back into the coop.

12. Skating on the Bog Ditch

Although William didn't care for hockey or rink skating, he did like skating on the bog because it appealed to his exploring instinct. In deep winter the excitement was in finding out how many miles up the main drainage ditch the skaters could go before they were stopped by snowdrifts across the ice. In the early spring, whole miles of the bog were covered with water that froze during the night; the next morning a skater had an immense feeling of freedom as he cruised down the expanse.

Sometimes the water near the great spring would be too warm to allow the ditch to freeze solid; these weak spots stopped the skaters. William took tumbles when his skate got caught in reeds. Once, a friend of Winnie's broke through and got wet up to her middle. She walked all the way home with her clothes frozen like a suit of armor.

13. Hauling Firewood

Hauling firewood was one chore that William never got to like. He could carry the wood by armfuls to the house from the woodpile, but that meant too much trudging through the snow. Better to load up a sleigh, and if John and Winnie would push or pull, that made it easier.

If for some reason the whole house had to be warmed, a full wagonload of wood had to be thrown in through the cellar window. The octopuslike furnace gobbled up the poplar logs like twigs, so, usually, most of the house was left unheated.

William didn't venture into the cold rooms except when really necessary. Going to bed was one such necessity. He would run up the stairs, strip quickly to his longjohn underwear, and dive under the blankets. Making a tight curl-up cubbyhole for himself, he would breathe and breathe until his hot breath made it tolerably warm.

The kitchen, though, had to be heated without fail, for the stove fire cooked the meals, dried the snow-wet clothing, and melted snow to make soft water for the laundry. So hauling wood was a regular chore. If the woodpile was snowed in, William had to dig for the logs. Sometimes, on the way to the front door, Winnie drew the sleigh over a deep rut and the load would start to slip. Iron bars held the wood at the two ends, but they didn't stop it from slipping out the sides. "Whoa! Whoa!" he would yell, as was the habit of farm children playing Horse and Wagon.

14. The Blizzard

There was at least one blizzard every winter, and this winter it came unexpectedly. Shortly after four o'clock, as William was returning from school, it began to snow. At first it looked like an ordinary snowfall, but by the time he had done his barn chores, it was snowing more heavily and a wind had started up. "Maybe," Winnie said wistfully, "we'll not have to go to school tomorrow." At bedtime William heard the wind shrieking around his bedroom window, but he could see nothing, for the window was frosted over.

The next morning, all the outside was a howling whiteness that took his breath away when he stepped out. There would be no school for sure, because children had been known to lose their way and freeze to death in such a blizzard. Farmyard chores were kept to a minimum, but some had to be done. William raised his mackinaw collar as high as possible, shielded his face with his hand, and plunged through the snow to the chicken coop to gather eggs and give the chickens water.

Most of the time the children stayed in the house looking out now and then through a melted patch on the pane of the kitchen window. By the end of the second day they could contain themselves no longer. They dressed extra warmly and ventured out into the storm to examine the half-dozen places in and around the farmyard where the wind had sculpted extra-high drifts.

15. Sundogs and Sticky Iron

The big blizzard that came each winter was followed by an eerie silence. It was partly an illusion, a contrast to the howling fury the ear had got used to after three days and nights. The wind had stopped and the sun was dazzling over the crisp, fresh, white landscape. In the clear air the train running three miles to the west of the farm sounded as if it were chugging down the highway, just up the lane.

As William went out on an errand, he noticed another odd thing. The sun had two little snippets of rainbow some distance away from it, just above the horizon. His father referred to this in Ukrainian: "The sun has ears," he said. But the other children in school with William knew they were called sundogs.

The double tree of the winter sleigh was broken, so William had to fetch one off a summer wagon. He waded through snow and tried to lift the bolt that held it to the wagon tongue, but his thick mitts were too clumsy. Forgetfully, he slipped one off and grabbed the bolt with his fingers. "Yayk!" he gasped. His fingers had stuck to the metal and it burned like fire. He shook it and shook it. Finally, it came off without tearing his skin. That was a 40°-below-zero lesson he did not forget that winter!

16. Snowdrift Fun

Back at school after the blizzard, the children could hardly wait until recess to explore the drifts. The biggest ones were against the bush to the northwest of the schoolyard. The wind had swept the snow there from across two miles of open fields. The bush broke the force of the wind and the snow settled in its twigs and branches, where it lay loosely packed. On the drift's surface the snow was packed and glazed, but once you broke through that upper crust, either by shoveling or jumping up and down on it, the rest of the way was easygoing.

The drifts were so high the children could make two-story apartments by honeycombing the snow with tunnels and caves. If they came in from the top they kept kicking their feet downward and then southward until they emerged into the open on the face of the drifts. At the elbow of the tunnel William and his companions carved out a meeting room for both girls and boys. Bright sunlight, reflecting off the tunnel walls, even lit the chamber dimly. So happily absorbed were the pupils in their building that they didn't hear the small school bell. The teacher had to use the big bonger up in the belfry to get them to return, cheeks glowing, to their desks. Their outer clothes, packed with snow in every crease, were left to dry by the boxstove in the corner.

17. Milk Truck on Snowplowed Road

Following the big blow, the road to the town five miles away was plugged
solid with drifts that reached as high as the telephone wires. Milk had to be got to
the city, and everyone — the farmer, the creamery, the trucker — wanted
it to get there.

Eventually, a snowplow would batter its way through the east-west line, pushing
enormous banks of snow to left and right. It had extra wing-type snow
scrapes to push the tops of the furrows farther away, so they would not slide down
and fill up the road again.

The newly cleared road looked like an open tunnel with room for just one
vehicle to pass through it. Saturday morning, as William went to town with his
father in their sleigh wagon, they met the milk truck coming toward them.
The driver gunned his motor, sending clouds of powdered snow billowing up behind
him, as he rushed to beat them to the crossroads and turn into a dairy farm
so they could get by.

A week later another, smaller, snowstorm filled the road to the top once more,
and the snowplow gave up. The farmers then had to haul their milk by
horse and sleigh over the tops of the drifts to meet the milk truck at the main
highway.

18. Snowball Weather

There was something different about the snow on balmy late winter days: it was no longer powdery. Then, not even hockey could hold the attention of William's schoolmates. Everyone wanted to make snowballs. Sometimes a snowman was made, but that was thought to be kids' stuff. Competition and marksmanship were the thing. The children threw as far as possible to knock each other's hats off, or they organized sides — if anything that came so naturally can be called organization — for a snowball war.

Sometimes forts were built first. A small mound of snow was made and rolled across the yard. It picked up the sticky snow under its weight and got fatter and fatter, until in time at least three people were needed to push it. That would be big enough! By then it had to be on location.

As a rest from pushing, William knelt and made ammunition. Snowballs were made most easily and firmly with bare hands. When his hands got too cold, he would put his flopping wet mitts on again and return to pushing the rest of the fort together.

In the war that followed, collars and scarves were loosened, caps came off, and mitts were lost. The children were all very wet and panting when they went back into the school after lunch.

19. Testing Depth of Spring Run-off

Spring was on its way when most of the snow had gone from the
schoolyard and the little that remained lay in drifts along the fences. The ice on
the rink became too "rubbery" for skating, but the hockey enthusiasts
played on in their boots. It was a time of year when William liked to go off by
himself to explore the water holes. He was fascinated by spring run-off
water. He never knew from day to day how deep it was, so he had to test it —
just as mountains have to be climbed.

Testing was risky, but that was part of the thrill. Ice or snow beneath the surface of the water might suddenly give, and then he had a rubber boot full
of icy cold water. Out he would scramble, for even one dry foot was better than
none. He emptied the boot, tugged off the soaking sock, and wrung it out.
The trouser leg could be wrung a little against the leg, or slipped down over the
outside of the boot.

William had early experiences of wettings — against his will. Older boys
would bully the youngest during recess to test the spring ice on the ditch in front
of the school. They would break through, of course, and the teacher would
have to dry out their clothes behind the school stove. Now that William was grow-
ing older, he remembered — and got no one wet except sometimes himself.

20. Return of the First Crow

Melting snow and ice were proof that winter was over, but William really
dated spring from an event that occurred a month earlier. It is said that the robin
is the first sign of spring. But on the prairies many say it's the prairie
horned lark, a small cousin of the meadow lark, that heralds spring. At the very
first thaw, these larks can be seen, sometimes in twos and threes, standing
beside puddles in the field. For William, however, there was something special
about the crow — perhaps because of its very noisy, very noticeable departure
at the beginning of winter — that made its return spell *spring* for him. Maybe too,
it was because the crow is a large bird, and black, so it stood out against the snow.

Crows came back singly, or in pairs, about the end of March. It was then
they were sighted by the children on their way to or from school. The lucky first-
sighters threw up their hands, and even their caps, in exultation, chanting,
"I saw it! I saw it! I saw the first crow! Spring's here!"

a prairie boy's summer

paintings and story by William Kurelek

With love for my sister Nancy

Who more than anyone else shared with me the surprise and wonder
of prairie seasons as a child

Who has added to that surprise and wonder a sense of awe and love for
the Creator of those wonders. Many call it the Living Whole —
Ultimate Cause — Nature. We two call it: God

a prairie boy's summer

1. Practicing for Field Day

In June, which Westerners regard as the beginning of summer, school was drawing to a close. William half regretted it, for summer always meant a lot of farm work, a lot more than in winter. At school there were three play recesses. True, it was also exam time; but he was always top of his class and the teacher sometimes even let him do his studying out in the grass by his lonesome.

One thing about June that William didn't look forward to was the last day of school — field day — when his school got together with two others in the district to decide which of the three would win The Shield that year for athletic strength and skill. In the last two weeks, training for it got really serious, and the teacher took time off to direct and record her pupils' progress.

There was no way to hide the fact kids even younger than William could run faster and jump farther and higher than he could. So he preferred the novelty races like the sack race, the three-legged race or the wheelbarrow race. He even liked the undignified peanut race in which the contestants had to get down on all fours and push a peanut along the ground with their noses. But William had one consolation. His school rivals during the rest of the year were now on his side. He knew they wanted him to do well in the competitions so The Shield could be won for their school.

2. Softball

In June it seemed to William they played baseball at school every day. He
wasn't as quick or strong as the other boys his age so he didn't care for baseball. He
preferred less competitive games like "bat'er-up" or "21 and in." But when sides
were chosen for baseball even the small kids had to play, because there were seldom
more than 25 children in the one-room school. A softball, about twice the size of
a hardball, was used, and even though it was softer, it still stung William's hands,
especially when it was new.

William offered to play an unimportant position like second base or midfield.
He stood there and daydreamed of making a sensational catch that would gain the
respect and admiration of the others. Suddenly he had to snap back to reality
for someone had hit the ball and it was high in the air heading toward midfield.
The opposing team yelled "Miss it! Miss it!" There were even catcalls to rile
him! "Butterfingers! You can't catch!" He ran under the ball and made a flying leap
with arms outstretched. The sun was in his eyes. So do you think he caught it?

3. School Lunch under the Woodpile

In winter the children had to eat their sometimes frozen sandwiches at their school desks. But in summer they had a bigger choice of lunch places. One of the boys' favorite spots was under the school woodpile. It offered just the right amount of shade if the day was hot, and it cut down the wind that tugged at their lunch wrapping.

William was a fussy eater and wasn't always excited about the contents of the black metal lunch box he shared with John. He always seemed to be getting peanut butter, which stuck to the roof of his mouth. Or corn syrup. Or homemade jam which had soaked right through the bread by lunchtime. Or hard-boiled eggs that choked him. Or else the butter was too thick. Baloney was all right if the bread hadn't been soaked with French mustard. Milk from a thermos helped the sandwiches go down. He was fond of dessert but he didn't get it often.

William preferred the fancy sandwiches — like brown sugar and butter — that came out of the lard pails and brown paper bags of his poorer neighbors and sometimes he persuaded them to swap. Once in a long while a wonderful smell rose out of his lunch box when it was opened, and he knew he was in for a treat. Real British Columbia apples which his father occasionally bought on his trips to town for the mail and farm supplies.

4. The Field Day

William couldn't escape it. The last day of school — field day — came. If his school was competing at one of the other schools, they were driven there in the back of a farm truck. The officials were usually teachers and school trustees, and competition was by age or sex or grade. A starting line was made in the grass with lime, and the finish line was a tightly held string. All toes were on the line as the official called out "One for the money. Two for the show. Three to get ready. And four to GO!" Away they went. William could see the backs of the fast runners pulling away from him. If he heard some slower unfortunate clomping along behind, he took comfort.

A lot of parents came and there was a picnic in the shade behind the school. The jumping and novelty races came after lunch. Winners earned points for their school and money for themselves: 15 cents for first place, 10 cents for second and 5 cents for third. Losers, like William, had to bring money from home to spend in the confection booth which had been built out of poplar branches against the outside wall of the school barn.

At the wheelbarrow race William heard someone shout: "Hey, look at that pair out front. The barrow's being carried! He's just pretending to touch the ground. Disqualify them!"

The day ended with two baseball games. If a school won both games it usually took The Shield because a ball game was worth the most points. William's school won it most often because it had the most pupils. It didn't seem exactly fair.

5. Swallows Dive-bombing the Cat

The first cat they had on the farm was called simply "Kitka" which is Ukrainian for cat.

William remembered her playing around the stove when she was only a kitten. She produced many litters in the seven years that she lived. Seven is a ripe old age for a farm cat, so she had a special warm spot in the family's heart, and was tolerated in the farmhouse. All the other cats had to live in the barn.

When Kitka saw William's mother leaving for the barn at milking time she'd set out ahead, knowing there'd soon be fresh warm milk.

However Kitka had enemies there — barn swallows. Their nests were half cones of mud glued to the sides of beams, close to the ceiling. A cat hadn't the slightest chance of getting a swallow unless a baby fell to the floor, but the swallows, William was amused to note, hated even the sight of a cat. When Kitka was still a good way off in the yard the swallows would begin dive-bombing her. Wheeling into formation high in the air, they'd zoom down to within a foot of her head, and scream rude swallow words into her ears. Kitka's tail would twitch angrily but she kept right on her course, pretending not to notice. She was plotting nonetheless, for once in a while she'd make a leap into the air and try to paw one of the bombers to the ground. She never succeeded, because they were too fast for her.

Meanwhile John, Winnie and William were at the barn door riling up the cows so they'd drop their droppings before going into the barn. But they must not be made too nervous or they would withhold their milk.

6. Catching Baby Killdeer

William and John loved birds. So when they were sent to fetch the herd at milking time they made sure the cows didn't step on a killdeer's nest they knew of near the barn road. A killdeer's nest lies flat, naked and exposed on the ground, and this one was so cleverly camouflaged that William had found it only by accident. One day as he was passing the mother bird flew up, then fell to the ground some yards away, crying and fluttering, pretending her wing was broken. He knew from the extra-big fuss she made he must be very close to her nest.

On this particular evening the herd scared the mother bird up again and William was delighted to see that the eggs had hatched! Darling fluffy little bits of life, standing high on legs thinner than toothpicks, scattered in all directions. Not yet able to fly they tripped on blades of grass and William caught one easily. He could feel the teeny heart going pit-a-pat in his hand. He knelt there trying to soothe it by stroking and talking. "Please, I'm not going to hurt you. I just want to hold you for a minute." How he wished he could tell the frantic mother that he wouldn't dream of harming her babies.

"Hey, get those cows in!" His mother shouted from the garden where she was hoeing out the weeds in the cabbages. William let the bird go, knowing it would reunite with its family at the nest when he had gone and they felt safe again.

7. Pasturing Cows

Before his father could afford to put an electric fence around his temporary
pastures, William often had to look after the cows all day. This wasn't a bad job if
the cows were satisfied and if the farm dog stayed with him to help, because then
he could read a pulp Western novel Steve lent him at school and daydream he was a
cowboy of the American frontier.

But faraway fields always look greener to a cow, and even when the pasture offered
enough to eat, the herd sometimes got restless. William swore they plotted their
escape, for they pretended to graze as they moved right up to a grain or cornfield.
Then, in less time than it took him to read another line and find out if his hero
had escaped the ambush, there they were in the forbidden field.

Sometimes William tried an ambush of his own to teach the cows a lesson. He'd
hide at the edge of the cornfield, and as soon as he heard the clicking of ankles and
snortlike breathing of the grazing herd, he'd let fly with his slingshot at the
lead cow. Once he struck her between the eyes with a pebble and she raised her
head in the air and shook it about as if dazed. William panicked. Had he permanently
injured her? What would his parents say? To his relief she soon rejoined the
retreating herd. But half an hour later the lesson wore off, and the herd was once
more edging its way back to the cornfield.

8. Burning Quack Grass and Harrowing

During the hot dry days of summer William got to know other Western weeds besides the ones often found in the garden. This season between sowing and harvest was the time to summer fallow — to work the land that was resting from bearing crops.

First, the field was plowed to bury the grasses and weeds so that they would die and turn into a kind of fertilizer. Then harrows, discs or spring-tooth cultivators were used to pull out any weeds that survived the plowing. These were left for the hot sun and wind to dry out.

The toughest weed to kill was called "quack grass" or "couch grass." Its roots were long and stringlike and they caught onto the soil even though they were torn out and lying on the surface. If there was enough moisture the quack grass put out both roots and green shoots and, if you left them alone long enough, they soon formed a whole colony or patch in the field. Quack grass roots had to be raked or harrowed together and burned. It was a tiring, dusty job walking after the harrows all day and William's shoulder ached from lifting each section when its spikes got clogged with roots.

Stacking and burning the piles of roots left by the harrow was more fun. William made a game of this. Although he had a box of matches in his pocket, he tried to avoid using them by carrying fire on his pitchfork from one pile to another. He had to run to get it across in time — but not so fast that his speed blew the fire out.

In the distance William could see clumps of bushes quivering and floating as if in a vast lake. This was a heat mirage, and the little whirlwinds that sprang up now and then in the field had an odd Ukrainian name: "a devil's wedding."

9. Haying

Haying was an important early summer job on dairy farms. When his father went into dairying William had to learn the many steps necessary to make a haystack out of a field of grass.

William's father planted his own grass, unlike his neighbors who rented sections of the bog to the east and cut natural grass. William envied the neighbors' boys for they sometimes stayed out on the bog for two whole weeks, cooking out in the open and sleeping under the wagon just like gypsies. He could see their stacker machine throwing hay up onto huge stacks on the horizon. William's father didn't have one, so their stacks were handbuilt and low.

The mower was the first machine used in haying, and it had to be oiled often. Its steady clatter made William sleepy, and only near accidents — like almost cutting a frog in half with the blade — kept him awake. In wet years there were lots of frogs. William liked the smell of fresh-mown hay, but he didn't like the job of raking the dried hay into bundles, first one way, then the other.

The next step, called sweeping, William was not allowed to do, because John had tried it one day and had an accident. The sweeper was like a giant comb on wheels between two horses. It pushed the hay bundles to the center of the field so that a stack could be built there. The horses were jittery because of horseflies and had to wear wire baskets to protect their tender noses. John's horses bolted from the horseflies, pulling the sweeper with its load of hay so fast that it overturned and rode over him. Only the hay into which he fell saved him.

William had to learn to build the stack right and at the same time catch more bundles of hay thrown up to him by his father and mother. Once they left a stack of clover unfinished and an approaching thunderstorm that night forced them to get up at 2 a.m. to put a peak on the stack. They saved the stack but not themselves from the downpour. Tired and sleepy and looking like drowned rats they got back to the house at dawn.

10. Thunderstorm Approaching

William loved the excitement of a thunderstorm during the day. It usually came in the afternoon after a hot sultry morning. This day his mother had been watching the dark cloud form and begin its swift approach. She yelled to the children, "Go round and close all the doors in the yard! Get the poultry in!" She was raising turkeys as well as geese and chickens that year. Turkeys are not as stupid as chickens and can be herded easier. Winnie and William went after them.

The dark sky cracked open with a crooked dagger of lightning. William instinctively drew in his neck; he knew that when a storm was that close, the thunderclap would follow hard on the flash. It came — WHOMP! The earth seemed to tremble from the crash. He liked the after-rumble, as the echo resounded between earth and heaven.

It was only at night that thunderstorms really frightened him. On the prairies they sometimes lasted all night. Even though the house had lightning rods he didn't trust them to keep the lightning from setting fire to the house.

Of course he knew the farm safety rule about not standing under a tree for shelter. Yet when he was working in the fields, it was a big temptation to avoid a soaking by heading for the clump of very tall trees in the field across the road. William had actually been hit by lightning once when he was closing a gate during the first few drops of rain. Fortunately it wasn't too big a jolt for it had already traveled a mile down the barbed-wire fence. William dropped the gate and ran.

11. Corn Cultivating

In the district where William grew up, dairy farmers raised corn for ensilage.
The livestock ate the stalk, not the cob, so the farmers grew a special hybrid corn
that produced little or no cob. This corn had to be cut while still green and
chopped up into the silo or ensilage hole before it had dried all out. It would then
ferment from its own moisture and weight.

But even early in the summer, when it was only a foot high, the corn needed special
attention. It had to be hilled and weeded. William's father bought a new cultivator and
after he himself had learned to work it, he put William on it. William didn't like
working on farm machines because the monotony put him to sleep. But he had to be
alert on this job; if his shoe slipped on one of the two foot levers he'd find to his
dismay the shovels below were digging up corn instead of weeds.

After a while William got good at the job and he could let himself daydream a
little. His father had promised him that when he passed grade nine he and John would
go to a high school in the big city. One of his daydreams was of being surrounded
by city high school students who listened in admiration to his stories of farm adventures.

How mistaken his daydreams turned out to be! The city boys weren't interested
in nature and didn't care to hear his stories. Many years would pass before William
found a way to get people interested.

12. Milking Time

Milking was a job William didn't look forward to, especially on hot, fly-filled days.

Outside there might be a blue sky and perhaps a refreshing breeze, but inside, the barn was like a furnace. To get at the teats on the far side of the cow's udder he had to lean tight against the cow's belly, which heaved and radiated heat like a big oven. Adding to the discomfort of the sweat, flies used his head and hands as a landing field. William had to be ready to grab the pail of milk away in case the cow kicked at a fly and put her foot in the pail. She used her tail as a fly swatter, too; and its coarse, dirty hairs often slapped William right across the back of the neck. He'd spray the cow with flytox, but its effect soon wore off. It was best when his little sister Nancy held the tail.

As relief from the milking ordeal, William amused himself by squirting one of the barn cats that waited nearby, meowing for its evening ration. It would jump away as if upset, but really it liked the white shower; for it sat down further off and set about licking away the milk.

If William's mother — who was the best milker in the family — was away for some reason it meant he and John had ten cows each to milk. That night their wrists would ache so badly they couldn't sleep. Everybody was relieved when the family became prosperous enough to buy a set of milking machines.

13. The Swimming Hole

William, like many another prairie boy, never saw a large body of water till his midteens. He did have a place to swim though, after the older boys of the district widened the bog ditch to the east of his father's farm in one spot. They built a sod dam and even a rough diving platform. It was the neighborhood swimming hole from that summer on.

There was no sand on the bottom, only clay and mud. The boys could feel it squishing up between their toes but they couldn't see it because as soon as they jumped in, they raised clouds of sediment that made the water opaque as pea soup. William didn't dare open his eyes underwater. By late afternoon, when it was time to head home for milking, the cloud had flowed as far as the first bridge.

Two kinds of water creatures lived at either end of the swimming hole and William disliked them both. Black catfish with their peculiar whiskers hung around out of curiosity at the clear upper end, and the dam at the lower end was like an apartment for dozens of crayfish. William hated the thought of stepping on a crayfish but couldn't resist raising the sod once in a while to stare at them. Sometimes as a joke a crayfish or a frog would be put in a swimmer's shoe. Another trick was to hide a swimmer's clothes. This was rather mean because they all swam stark naked and the victim was left with nothing to wear home.

No one brought towels. After their swim, they ran around in the big field opposite the hole. When sun and wind had dried them, their bodies were covered with a fine, white coat of clay which they brushed off. Nobody lived way out on the bog, but they still had to keep one quarter of an eye open, for once in a rare while a gang of local girls would visit the bog on their bikes.

14. Making a Smudge

Apart from milking, dairying was much easier in summer than in winter. After his father put up an electric fence the cows took little looking after; all the boys had to do was pump a tankful of water for them.

But every summer evening, there was one more favor the cattle appreciated — especially in wetter years. Clouds of mosquitoes appeared — people said they came off the bog to the east — and William's parents would send him out at sunset to build a smudge fire to protect the animals from the pests.

Making a smudge wasn't the same as making a bonfire though it was sometimes called that. William's father showed him how to mix layers of dry straw with layers of wet straw or manure so that the pile would glow and smoke instead of blaze. Otherwise the fire would burn out long before daylight and the cattle would be unprotected. Of course, if there was no breeze the smoke didn't help much, for it went straight up. But that didn't happen very often.

William found there were really no gentlemen in the animal world. Even if the cows got to the smudge first, the farm horses always came along and took away the best places in the smoke. The cows knew the horses were bullies, so they moved out of the way before they were bitten or pushed aside.

15. Plowing

Plowing was a long, lonely job. On the old tractor William didn't fall asleep so easily because its steel wheels made for a rough ride. But the new tractor had rubber tires and there was only the noise of its two cylinders to keep him awake. "Bach, bach — bach, bach" its exhaust repeated over and over all day long and even after supper till it was completely dark. As long as William could still make out the furrow he had to keep plowing.

William's father adjusted the plow levers to the right depth, and because the tractor was new it hardly ever broke down. The only excuse for stopping was when Nancy brought out some water or lunch. Or if the fuel was low. William didn't dare turn off the motor because he didn't have the knack of turning the flywheel to start it up again. One time, after trying for two hours and getting blisters all over his hands, he had to go out on the bog to fetch his friend Billie to help him.

Nor was William strong enough to tip the fuel barrel to fill the fuel can with distillate. This was a cheaper, less refined fuel than gasoline and was used only in tractors. Sometimes he siphoned it by sucking on the end of the hose, but occasionally he got a mouthful of it and didn't like the taste. Another way he got the siphon going was to insert the hose into the barrel, holding his hand tight over the other end. Then he would pull the hose out and down very quickly. If he was lucky the fuel would start to flow itself.

Making turns on the tractor was easy enough after the first year of bungling. William also got the knack of pulling the trip rope to raise the plow when he reached the end of a furrow or to drop it after making the "E" turn. A flock of gulls followed him as he plowed to gobble up the worms and bugs the plow turned up.

16. Cutting Grain

William was only twelve when his father drafted him and John into harvest work. He might have had another year or two to grow stronger and more capable if the war hadn't come and taken away all his father's hired hands. Another sign of the war was the bombers that began to appear in the sky from the direction of the city airfield. They practiced dropping their bombs far out on the bog to the east and then they circled back over the farm toward the city.

At first William was put on the old black tractor, which pulled two binders. His father rode on the front one, John on the second. The old binders broke down a lot, so William had to be ready to make a quick stop when his father yelled "Whoa!" To make up for time lost repairing equipment, they had to cut grain well into the night, even after the moon rose. William and John were so dead tired they fell into bed without even washing off the field dust.

The second year was easier. By then the old tractor had broken down completely and his father bought a new, bright green one. Now they had time to look around and enjoy watching prairie animal life. As a patch of grain still uncut in the middle of the field grew smaller and smaller all kinds of creatures ran out — partridges, gophers, rabbits, skunks. The farm dog was always on hand, hopeful for game, but he hardly ever caught anything. Rabbits ran too fast, and he had learned by painful experience not to get too close to a skunk.

Nancy was just strong enough that year to carry water out to the workers in the field. They appreciated it, for cutting grain was hot, dry work.

17. Stooking

Some years there were wet spells even during harvest time. It wouldn't actually rain — just turn foggy and drizzly, but too much moisture wasn't good for the grain. Wet grain, or grain that had sprouted, was good only for cattle feed. Gray weather made William sad.

If the grain was too wet to cut, the family could still stook for a while. William's mother was a good stooker and taught him how to do it properly. You picked up two sheaves, held them either by the binder twine or under your arm and then brought them down firmly to the ground with their tops together, leaning against each other. Another two pairs of sheaves brought down in the same way, on either side of the first two, completed the stook. A stook was shaped like a teepee so the rain would run off it, and it had a hole in the middle so the wind could dry it inside.

When stooking, everyone wore long sleeves and, if possible, trousers and even gloves to protect himself from stubble and straw scratches. William hated barley because the sheaves were small and sometimes fell apart, and their beards scratched his face. The thing he dreaded most was getting a barley beard in his mouth or throat. It irritated like anything and it took some fishing with his fingers to get it out.

In wet years there were also more mice than usual. They had to be killed because of all the grain they would eat. William and his mother heard John yell "A mouse!" and saw him chase after it. The mouse might succeed in hiding in the next row of sheaves, but it got caught when that row was being stooked.

18. Mending Pigs' Fence

It seemed that a large part of William's life on the farm was spent capturing escapees. Horses, bulls, chickens, calves, pigs — all had their "prison breaks." Pigs caused William the most trouble. Because they are such notorious wanderers, they were penned inside a page-wire fence. But they are also notorious rooters so every few days they'd dig under the fence and escape, heading for parts unknown. When William finally found them, it was hard to herd them back. Eventually, of course, most escapees got hungry and came back to be fed.

But the family had a faster way to get the pigs back — as long as at least one pig was left in the pen. William's father would twist its leg or ear, and it would squeal loud and long. A pig's hearing is very sharp, and soon William would see the whole herd come charging back from the other end of the farm to defend their brother in distress. As soon as they rushed in through the open gate or through the hole they'd dug, the innocent one would be released from his tortures.

Then William and John had the job of repairing the fence. While the boys worked, the pigs stood at a distance in the weeds, sniffing and snorting and watching with their mischievous little eyes. "Look at them," said William. "I bet they're figuring how to undo this repair job!"

19. Gopher Hunting

School always opened on the first of September. All through the summer holidays the schoolhouse seemed to sleep, as if resting from the beating the kids had given it the last school year, and gathering strength for the new one in the fall. Weeds managed to grow high in front of the school buildings, and out in the tall grass gophers dug their burrows. Gophers are pests to farmers. When there were too many of them the municipality even paid kids a one-cent-a-tail bounty for them.

When the boys returned to school, they kept their eyes open for gophers and as soon as they spotted one they formed a hunting posse. Some had stones and clubs. Others carried pails of water. Often a dog from a nearby farm joined the chase. A gopher usually escaped the first pail of water poured down the hole by emerging from a second, backdoor hole. "There she goes!" yelled William as she scampered to another hole. They had to act fast then, for they knew that the gopher realized she was in danger of drowning and would quickly build a dam below ground. The boys always knew if she succeeded because only a little water went in before the hole was full. But if bubbles came up they knew they had her. She'd surface, wet and miserable, and try to escape by running between the legs of the attackers to still another hole. William sometimes felt a twinge of pity for her. But a pest is a pest. Blinded and confused she'd run around in circles under a rain of stones, sticks and clubbings until someone made a direct hit and finished her off.

20. Bows and Arrows

Threshing time was a sure sign autumn was taking over after summer. Already there was a certain chill in the air at night. From the schoolyard William could see bright new straw stacks rising here and there on the horizon. His father's were the most numerous, for he still prided himself on being a grain farmer. A threshing scene is exciting even at a distance. William felt a little guilty enjoying his recess when it was the busiest season for his parents on the farm. But he knew they excused him, for his father thought education even more important than farm work.

William enjoyed his recesses more than usual the year he was twelve because the other boys had gone along with a new sport he introduced — archery. William had a natural knack for carving and his bows and arrows were the best for distance and accuracy. At last, here was a sport in which he excelled.

William had read about a way of using the feet to shoot. So they all sat down to try it, and sure enough it worked. The arrows went clear out of the schoolyard into the pasture on the other side of the highway. It seemed the boys were conquering the awesomeness of the prairie expanses at last.

In another two years William too would be leaving the grassy schoolyard — for the concrete and cinders of a city high school playground.

William Kurelek grew up on the prairies during the hard 1930s.
The first several years of his life were lived on a grain
farm in Alberta, Canada, where his father had settled after coming from
the Ukraine. Then the family moved to a dairy farm in Manitoba, not
far from the United States border, which is the setting of this book.

Later, when William Kurelek was sixteen, he was sent to high school
in the city, where he was eager to tell his new friends about his adventures living close to nature. No one seemed interested in listening
and it was many years before Kurelek found a way to hold an audience —
through his pictures.

William Kurelek's paintings are represented in major art museums
in Canada, the United States, and England.

Awards won by William Kurelek's books

a prairie boy's winter

A *New York Times* Best Illustrated Book of 1973
A *New York Times* Outstanding Book of 1973
Canadian Association of Children's Librarians' Best Illustrated Book, 1974
Showcase Book Award, 1974
Boston Globe/Horn Book Honor Book, 1974
Third International Survey of Children's Book Illustration, *Graphis*, The Graphis Press, Zurich, Switzerland
One of only 4 books out of 2000 chosen by 3 independent juries (retailers, designers and children) of the American
 Institute of Graphic Arts as best children's books published in the US and Canada, 1973-4

a prairie boy's summer

A *New York Times* Outstanding Book of 1975
Showcase Book Award, 1976
Canadian Association of Children's Librarians' Best Illustrated Book, 1976
IODE Book of the Year, 1976
Chosen by Toronto Public Libraries as one of the Top 100 Canadian Children's Books, 1977

lumberjack

A *New York Times* Best Illustrated Book, 1974
A *New York Times* Outstanding Book of the Year, 1974
American Institute of Graphic Arts, 50 Books of the Year, 1974
An American Library Association Notable Children's Book, 1974
A Children's Book Council Showcase Book, 1974
One of 16 Outstanding Books of Decade, chosen by John Goldthwaite for *Harper's*

a northern nativity

American Institute of Graphic Arts Certificate of Excellence, chosen for "Books 76"
A *Kirkus* Choice: one of the 50 Best Books of 1976
An American Library Association Notable Children's Book, 1976
Chosen by Toronto Public Libraries as one of the Top 100 Canadian Children's Books

COLLINS